Dads c
Mums

Kasia Reay

Illustrated by Lucy Banaji

Schofield&Sims

My mum is good with wood.

My dad is such a good cook.

My mum is good with a duck and a hook.

Look! My dad is good with his foot.

My mum is good with wool.

Look at this! This is me...

I am good with a book!